Deluxe Edition   1932
1/777
(from 1740 Original)

PB

Merryland

THIS DE LUXE EDITION OF MERRYLAND IS NARROWLY LIMITED TO SEVEN HUNDRED SEVENTY-SEVEN COPIES

MERRYLAND

BY
THOMAS STRETZER

PRIVATELY ISSUED

NEW YORK

ROBIN HOOD HOUSE

Copyright, 1932, by
ROBIN HOOD HOUSE
New York

PRINTED IN THE UNITED STATES OF AMERICA

To George Cheyne

SIR,

IT *is my misfortune not to have the honor of a personal acquaintance with any great man, to whom, with a tolerable grace, I could apply the usual panegyric, which custom has made so necessary an ingredient in Dedications; but turning my thoughts to those, with whose learned works and labors for the public good, I am better acquainted, than with their persons, you, sir, immediately occurred as the properest patron for the following work.*

Whether I consider you as an eminent physician, as a member of that learned society, of which you are also one of the greatest orna-

Dedication

ments, or as a philosopher, endowed with an infinite fund of knowledge in natural and experimental philosophy; whatever light I view you in, your accomplishments are so resplendent, so universally known and admired, that no lustre can be added to them by the greatest encomiums. Their intrinsic excellence takes away all possibility of flattery, and I blush as much at my incapacity of giving you your just due, as you would at ascribing more than they deserved, to others.

These considerations make this work your peculiar property, and are very urgent inducements for addressing it to you, especially, as I have thereby the advantage of exempting myself from that hardship which attends most dedicators, of inventing the virtues they celebrate.

To do justice to your great abilities, both as a physician and philosopher, to describe

Dedication

your amiable genteel address and polite behavior, your generous contempt of money, and abhorrence of adulation, with the rest of your "Christian virtues, which are not only universally admired, but felt," would be a task too difficult for any sentient or intelligent being, incumbered with the adamical crust of clay, and can never be executed with infallibility and impeccability, but by those who, after a progressive purification, are developed and mundified of that plaister or vehicle of a denser and coarser element, superinduced over the primitive æthereal body, by which the spirits are infinitely condensed, concentered and incrassated.

Your learned works, sir, deriving from their author a ray, efflux, or infinitesimal emanation, are above the reach of critics, and by sending this into the world under your patronage, I hope the extreme tenderness

Dedication

and delicacy of its lumbaginous state will be protected from the noxious and deleterious qualities of those envious wretches, "the powers of whose souls are sunk, concentered, imprisoned, and contracted to a punctum saliens, *by their unformed tabernacle or organical vehicle, and cannot exert their intellectual functions." These critics "have, by wrong or no culture, stunted the organs of their faculties, and by a perpetual* malregimen *distorted them; and like our planet, have so many untoward and oblique symptoms of a designed deteriority, that they are not fit to commerce with our bodies: like the scuttle-fish, they spout out their own black liquor on the pellucid element." In return for these bad qualities, I wish them no other exacerbation, or anything more deleterious, than a strict confinement to an abstemious* vegetable regimen, *and an* aqueous beverage.

Dedication

I shall not make any farther intrusion on your precious time, or divert it longer from your philosophical studies, but submit the following work to your perusal at a leisure hour.

As you are now past the meridian, and the "hyperbolic curve of life is at the point of returning downwards again," it is not to be expected you can enjoy the pleasure of making any more journies to MERRYLAND; *but "since all sentient and intelligent beings are made for happiness, and will by mere instinct seek it somehow or somewhere, I hope the following chapters will supply you with some suitable entertainment and amusement, with which your leisure hours may be agreeably diverted, while you continue in this lapsed, expiatory and progressive state," till you gradually put off this adamical tabernacle, and slide into another, according to the gen-*

Dedication

eral laws of purification, till at last you arrive at that fixed and permanent state designed for you in the universal system of intelligences.

I beg leave to assure you that I have the most "vehement willings, longings, volitions, and velleities," to approve myself,—Sir, your great admirer, most humble, and most obedient Servant,

THE EDITOR.

BATH, 20 Oct. 1740.

The Editor to the Reader

It *is become an observation, trite enough, that when any work like this, which is new and curious, makes its appearance in the world, almost everyone is desirous to have some account of the author.*

To satisfy therefore in some measure this common curiosity, I shall acquaint my reader with all that I have been able to learn concerning the writer of the following sheets.

His name I find to be Roger Pheuquewell, with the addition of Esq.; descended from an ancient family in Ireland, remarkable for their being red-headed, of great note, and of long standing in that country. He was the youngest brother of nine, and consequently

The Editor to the Reader

could have no great patrimony to begin the world withal, and therefore in the year 1717 he came to London to seek his fortune, as several of his relations had successfully done before him. He was then in the full vigor of youth, bless'd with great abilities, a good address, a most advantageous stature, and well proportioned graceful shape, and otherwise well qualified. All these advantages soon recommended him to the most inward favor of a rich widow, whom he in a short time married, and during her life was genteelly maintained by her jointure. He made frequent journies to Merryland in her lifetime; but after her death, he took a fancy to be almost continually going and coming, and spent so much in these journeys that he was reduced to very low circumstances, and retired at last to Boulogne in France, where he died on the 19th of April 1738, N.S., and at

The Editor to the Reader

his death the following sheets were found among his other papers.

He was lodged at a hotel in that town, the master of which had a near acquaintance with a capuchin friar, whom he called to his assistance in examining the papers of the deceased. To be short, the friar upon looking some time into the manuscript, cried out to the landlord, "Here is a curiosity, I believe, that will pay, not only what is owing to you for bed and board, but will, over and above that, put money in your pocket;" and so he voluntarily offered to translate it into French for his benefit.

Accordingly this was done, but the capuchin not being a sufficient master of the English tongue to do justice to the author, the book was published with so many errors and mistakes, that the writer himself, had he been alive, could not have known it for his own.

The Editor to the Reader

Its first step into the world (thus deformed) was no longer after the author's death than the middle of the following June, and notwithstanding all its blemishes, it met with so good a reception in France, that it is now some months since it went through the sixth edition at Paris.

Soon after the first publication, our author was so well relished in Madrid, that a Spanish translation was published there by Don Juan Compostella il Tarragona, dedicated to the Archbishop of Saragossa, but this version was not less faulty than that of the friar.

An Italian has done the author more justice, for which reason it was thought he had, by some means or other, procured an English copy: this was published at Rome, in March 1739, and although the translator is not certainly known, it is supposed to be the

The Editor to the Reader

work of an eminent cardinal, whose name I am not at liberty to mention.

Nor was it long after, that a neat edition was published at Dantzick, in the Polish language, by one Venskousky Wisniawisky, and another about the same time in Danish, printed at Copenhagen, by Gaspar Gluckstat; not to mention the Dutch and German editions, which would be too tedious to enumerate in this place.

It may perhaps be allowed, that there is not a great deal to be said in commendation of our author's diction; but then it may be answered, that a work of so grave and serious a nature, could not well admit of those flowers and ornaments which embellish subjects of wit and humor. However, it is more than probable, he would have corrected the style, as the last hand to the work, before he put it to the press, had not death prevented him.

The Editor to the Reader

Notwithstanding any accidental disadvantages that have attended this work, it has, like the palm, flourished in spite of all oppression. And it is evident that the surprisingly good reception it has met with, in so many different and so far distant countries, could not have happened, but from the truth and novelty of the subject. It would therefore be very difficult to account for anything so extraordinary, as that so valuable a piece should never have spoken its own language (if I may be allowed the expression) till this time; especially when we consider how many of our countrymen have been travelling abroad in the time of which we are speaking, how much diligence is daily made use of to procure anything that is new, in all parts of Europe; and lastly, that we have so many translators (of the French in particular) that hardly anything, new or old, can escape their

The Editor to the Reader

labor. *I am unwilling to attribute this long neglect in England of so valuable an author, to any greater depravity in our taste, or less relish for useful learning than our neighbors; though I am much afraid, our fondness for fairy tales, fabulous stories, monstrous fictions and romances, has of late years too much increased, and makes us take the less delight in studying such grave and serious books as this now before us.*

I shall detain the reader no longer but only to assure him that I have taken all possible care to make this edition correct, having luckily had an opportunity of seeing the original manuscript with which this was carefully collated.

Upon the whole, I think, I may reasonably hope to see this valuable work at last kindly received in England, and go through as many editions here, as it has done in France, and is likely to do in almost all the countries in Europe.

The Contents

Chapter I   *page* 39
    Of the Name of Merryland, and whence it is so called

Chapter II   *page* 45
    Of the Situation of Merryland

Chapter III   *page* 55
    Of the Air, Soil, Rivers, Canals, etc.

Chapter IV   *page* 69
    Of the vast Extent of Merryland, its Divisions and principal Places of Note

Chapter V   *page* 77
    Of the ancient and modern Inhabitants, their Manners, Customs, etc.

Chapter VI   *page* 85
    Of the Product and Commodities, such as Fish, Fowls, Beasts, Plants, etc.

Chapter VII   *page* 93
    Of the Rarities, Curiosities, etc.

Chapter VIII   *page* 103
    Of the Government of Merryland

Chapter IX   *page* 111
    Of the Religion

Chapter X   *page* 117
    Of the Language

The Contents

Chapter XI   *page* 123
    Of the several Tenures, etc.

Chapter XII   *page* 131
    Of the Harbors, Bays, Creeks, Sands, Rocks, and other dangerous Places, with the Settings and Flowings of the Tides and Currents; and safe Directions for Strangers steering into Merryland

Preface by the Author

FAVORED by indulgent Providence with twenty years' experience, and frequent opportunities of acquainting myself with the situation and circumstances of MERRYLAND, I have at length finished my inquiries into the present state of that country, and disposed the materials I have collected in such a manner as, I presume, will give everyone, who desires to be informed, a tolerable idea of the country I have described.

It must be confessed, however, there still remains some part of this delightful country undiscovered, and that there are many laws, customs, and curiosities, of which we have hitherto a very imperfect knowledge. Of

Preface by the Author

these I have chosen to say little or nothing, rather than amuse mankind with the uncertain guesses and fabulous relations of idle travellers, who observing the weakness of the generality of readers, and their gust for everything that carries an air of novelty and wonder, entertain them principally with whimsies of their own brains.

Since the world is no longer to be amused with the fabulous relations of travellers and historians, any more than with the dreams of superstition and enthusiasm; an attempt to distinguish truth from fiction, and to discover the certainty of those accounts we have received of MERRYLAND, it is presumed, will not be unacceptable to this discerning age. Relations monstrous and unnatural may please the weak and indolent, but truth and nature only can satisfy the wise: my design therefore is to examine what others have

Preface by the Author

published of this wonderful and delicious country, to compare them one with another, and with my own observations, in order to sift out the truth. And having searched narrowly into the state of this country myself, and been conversant with many people, whose inclinations led them to make inquiries, and whose good luck gave them frequent opportunities of satisfying their curiosities; I say, having made it my business to inform myself from all the intelligent travellers I have met with, and added their remarks to my own, I hope I shall not be deemed altogether unqualified for such an undertaking.

I need not say how useful and necessary a work of this nature will be to the world. I shall only observe that nobody has ever attempted it before in this method; and it is somewhat surprising, that all the modern geographers, such as Cluverius, Ortelius,

Preface by the Author

Cellarius, etc., should be entirely silent about so remarkable a country, which was discovered many years ago, and was well known to the ancients; as appears by Berosus a Chaldean, who wrote the History of Babylon in the time of Antiochus Soter; and Herodotus, the most ancient writer among the Greeks (whose works have reached us) speaks of this country as a place well known in those days. It is as certain too that the old Academics, Peripatetics, and Stoics, were tolerably well acquainted with this country, as appears by some of their own works as well as by the testimony of other authors; and the great Metrodorus, who was a scholar of Epicurus, was frequently there. Our English geographers take no notice of it; Mr. Moll in his Atlas has entirely omitted it, and the learned Mr. Gordon makes no mention of it, neither has Mr. Salmon said a word of it in his Mod-

Preface by the Author

ern History, or Present State of all Nations; nor have Mr. Cusshee or Mr. Senex given it a place in their Globes.

I cannot imagine these gentlemen so ignorant as to be entirely unacquainted that there is such a country; but as it is not my business to account for their omissions, I shall say no more of them, but that their silence has rendered this work of mine the more necessary. How well I have executed it, or how far it is still deficient, must be submitted to the candid and impartial reader. I shall not be at all surprised if some censorious people blame me for my bold attempt, and others find fault with the performance; this is what I expect, and am prepared for by that Distich of Mimnermus,

Oblectes Animum; plebs est morosa legendo,
Ille benè de te dicet, at ille malè.

I shall conclude this Preface with wishing

Preface by the Author

the reader may find all the pleasure and satisfaction he can desire in perusing this short work. If it affords him no improvement, I may venture to promise it will at least give him some entertainment. But lest anything I might say here should be suspected of partiality, I shall decline adding anything more of myself, but lay before my reader the following opinion of that truly learned and Right Reverend Prelate the Bishop of London, who says,

"Of all the studies to which men are drawn, either by inclination or interest, perhaps no one can pretend to such an agreeable pleasure as the Description of Countries. By a variety of prospects they feed us constantly with fresh satisfactions; and the objects they present are so chained together that a curious reader has much ado to break off. This is the advantage of that subject in

Preface by the Author

general." But when we come to affairs that nearly concern us, the relish is still heightened in proportion to everyone's love for the country treated of.

Chapter I

OF THE NAME OF MERRYLAND
AND WHENCE IT IS SO CALLED

THE names of most countries have been much altered from those they were formerly known by; and even to this day, different nations, nay, people of the same country, give different names to the same place. Merryland, like other countries, has been known under a great variety of names, and perhaps now has as various appellations as any part of the creation. It is not my purpose to trouble the reader with a long recital of them, nor to dispute which is the most proper; let it suffice in these pages to call it Merryland, so named (as the learned antiquarians inform us) from the Greek word μυρίζυο, *i.e. Unguentis inungo,* alluding to the unctuous nature of the soil, or perhaps to the practice of some people in that country, of whom historians say, *In Lætitiâ Unguentis utebantur, erantque* μεμιρισμένοι, *i.e. Unguentis et Oleo delibuti,* from the transporting delight that it gives. By the French it is called Terre-Gaillarde, from the Greek ἀγαλλιαάω, Lætitiâ exulto, or from γαί, Lætor. Either of these derivations seems to me very plausible, and has very significant reference to the wonderful delight people enjoy in Merryland, as will be more fully related in the succeeding chapters. However, far be it from me to presume absolutely to fix this derivation as infallible; it being a matter of great consequence to the learned world, I shall with all humility submit it to the more judicious determination of the learned and useful Society of Antiquarians. Meanwhile I am pretty much confirmed in the justness of this etymology by the High-German and Dutch names of Merryland, the first calling it **Frolich-landt**, and the other **Vrolick-landt,** both which agree in the same signification and, in my humble opinion, clear up the matter almost beyond dispute.

Chapter ii

OF THE SITUATION OF MERRYLAND

MERRYLAND is a part of that vast continent called by the Dutch geographers, the 𝔘𝔯𝔬𝔦𝔣-𝔩𝔞𝔫𝔡𝔱𝔰𝔠𝔞𝔭; it is situate in a low part of the continent, bounded on the upper side, or to the northward, by the little mountain called Mnsvnrs, on the east and west by Coxasin and Coxadext, and on the south or lower part it lies open to the terra firma.

There is something very remarkable and surprising as to the longitude and latitude of this country, neither of which could ever yet be fixed to any certain degree; and it is pretty evident, however strange it may seem, that there are as great variations both of the latitude and longitude in Merryland, as of the mariner's compass in other parts of the

Of the Situation of Merryland

world. To confirm this, I beg leave to assure the reader of a matter of fact which, if he be an entire stranger to Merryland, he will perhaps scarce have faith to believe; but they who have any tolerable experience and knowledge of the country, will be so far from discrediting, that I do not doubt but they will be ready to confirm it by their own observation.*

Know then, courteous reader, soon after my first entrance into this wonderful and delightful country (having as prying a curiosity as most men) I endeavored to get the best insight that was possible in everything relating to the State of Merryland, observing with diligent attention everything the country afforded that was remarkable either in

---

* But now attend; I'll teach thee something new,
'Tis strange, but yet 'tis reason, and 'tis true;
Ev'n what we now with greatest ease receive,
Seem'd strange at first, and we could scarce believe:
And what we wonder at, as years increase,
Will seem more plain, and all our wonders cease.
      CREECH's Lucret, B. II.

Of the Situation of Merryland

art or nature, all which I intend to communicate to the public in the following sheets. Among other things I made very accurate observations both of the latitude and longitude, and may venture to say, there could be no considerable mistake in my observations, as they were made with a proper instrument, of a large radius, and in perfect good order; nay, I have been assured, when I was in Merryland, that my instrument was inferior to none. But some years after, happening to be there again, and repeating the experiment, I found both latitude and longitude increased many degrees, though I tried in the same spot, and with the same instrument as before.

It may, perhaps, be suspected that my instrument might have suffered since the first experiment was made (as it is well known that the best are liable to damage by time and frequent use), but that was not the case; for though mine had, I must confess, been

Of the Situation of Merryland

often used, yet it was with such prudent care and caution, that it was in as great perfection as ever; and even at this day I could venture to recommend it as a tolerable good one, though I have had it above these thirty years, and used it pretty freely, and with great satistion to myself and others.

That the latitude and longitude then were evidently and considerably increased is a matter of fact beyond dispute; but how to account for so wonderful a phenomenon I must leave to others, and should think it well worthy the consideration of that curious and learned body, the Royal Society:

Felix, qui potuit rerum cognoscere Causas.
Virgil.

That they may have all the hints and information towards it, which my experience can afford, I must acquaint them that this surprising increase of latitude and longitude in Merryland seldom fails to happen, after having a fruitful season in that country (as had been the case when my experiment was last made) so much does it increase, that after a few years one would scarce believe he was in the same part of the world; nor is its fruitfulness the only cause of this variation; frequent tilling the soil, though it should prove utterly barren, or no seed be sown in it, is observed in some measure to produce the same effect.

This extraordinary alteration of the latitude is not at all agreeable, but the greater degree it extends to, the less delightful is the country to its inhabitants: on which consideration some projectors have been induced to try several methods (and as they pretend with success) for reducing the latitude, when too much augmented, and by that means restore Merryland, at least in appearance, to its primitive state; but they must be ignorant people indeed, who can be imposed on by such practices; yet such it seems there have been, but they are justly laughed at for their

Of the Situation of Merryland

credulity, and by nobody more, than by the very persons who so easily deceived them.

I need say no more of the situation of this country, but after the example of that excellent geographer, Mr. Patrick Gordon (who in his *Geographical Grammar* tells us what place is the Antipodes, or opposite part of the globe to the several countries he treats of) I shall conclude this chapter by informing the curious reader that the Antipodes to Merryland is by some said to be that prominent part of the continent called Pdx, known in High Dutch by a very common expression; others affirm the Antipodes to be in the very uttermost point of the Promontory Cpt; but it is not my intention to concern myself in these disputes, but stick as close as may be to my subject. I shall leave the affair of the Antipodes to those who have a taste that way; only I shall observe, there are some people who very preposterously (as I think) give the preference to the Pdx; the Italian geographers are pretty much inclined that way; some of the Dutch have likewise come into it, and of late years a few in Great Britain have appeared not altogether averse to it.

Chapter iii

OF THE AIR, SOIL, RIVERS, CANALS, ETC.

THE air in Merryland is very different, being in some provinces perfectly pure and healthy, in others extremely gross and pestilential; for the most part it may be said to be like the air in Holland, "generally thick and moist, by reason of the frequent fogs which arise from its lakes and canals," yet it is mostly very pleasant and agreeable to the inhabitants, though it cannot always be said to be wholesome. In the most healthful provinces it agrees well with young and vigorous constitutions; but for old men or those who are consumptive, this country is at best esteemed very pernicious, especially if they enjoy it too much, which many are tempted to by the bewitching pleasantness of the place, of which we may say with Solomon, "How fair and how pleasant art thou, O love, for delights!"

The climate is generally warm, and sometimes so very hot, that strangers inconsiderately coming into it have suffered exceedingly; many have lost their lives by it, some break into sores and ulcers difficult to be cured; and others, if they escape with their lives, have lost a member. It is certain there can be no distemper more to be dreaded than this, occasioned by the heat of the climate in Merryland; the curious may see it particularly described, with all its hideous symptoms, by our countryman Bartholomew Glanville (who flourished about the year 1360) in his book *De Proprietatibus Rerum,* translated by John Trevisa, Vicar of Barkeley, in 1398. But notwithstanding this inconvenience is so well known, so bewitchingly tempting is the country, that people will too frequently rush into it without caution or consideration of their danger; even those who know the ill consequence, from dear-bought experience, are not always deterred from precipitantly repeating the same folly; nay, so remarkable is this rashness in the inhabitants of Merryland, that it is become a common proverb to say "they have no forecast."

But this dangerous heat of the climate, with all its dreadful concomitants, is not so very terrible, but it may be guarded against by taking proper precautions, and people might venture into it without much hazard, even at the worst seasons, and in the most unhealthy provinces; they need no more to avoid the danger, but be careful always to wear proper clothing, of which they have a sort that is very commodious, and peculiarly adapted to this country; it is made of an extraordinary fine thin substance, and contrived so as to be all of one piece, and without a seam, only about the bottom it is generally bound round with a scarlet ribbon for ornament. This clothing has been found so useful, that a modern bard thought fit to write a poem in its commendation, and has most elegantly celebrated its praises in blank verse.

Sometimes the climate is as much on the other extreme, cold, to a great degree; but this rarely happens, nor has it any bad effect on the inhabitants, otherwise than by being disagreeable and uncomfortable to live in.

In general the country is warm enough, and so exceedingly delightful, that every man at first coming into it is transported with pleasure; the very sight of Merryland, or any near approach to it, puts one in strange raptures; and even in dreaming of it, people have enjoyed a most pleasing kind of delirium. In short, it is the loveliest and sweetest region of the world, and is thus painted by the poet:

Quas neq; concutiunt Venti, neq; Nubilæ Nimbis Aspergunt, neq; Nix acri concreta Pruina

Of the Air, Soil, Rivers, Canals, Etc.

*Cana cadens violat, semperq; innubilus Æther
Contigit et late diffuso Lumine ridet.**

However, I must own, the poet seems to have been a little too bold and hyperbolical in this description; and fond as I am of the country, I am not so partial as to think this poetic flight strictly justifiable, notwithstanding that all the learned commentators have written to reconcile it to truth:

Crescit in immensum facunda Licentia Vatum.†

The country lying very low (as Mr. Gordon says of Holland) its soil is naturally very wet and fenny, the parts that are best inhabited are generally the moistest; and naturalists tell us this moisture contributes much to its fruitfulness; where it is dry it seldom

---
* *Which, winds not ruffle, nor the humid train
Of gathering clouds e'er deluge o'er with rain;
Nor fleecy snow, nor frosts deform the soil,
Or frustrate, or suspend the lab'rour's toil;
Perpetual spring smiles on the fertile ground,
And genial suns diffuse their influence round.*

† *Poets claim licence that will know no bounds.*

Of the Air, Soil, Rivers, Canals, Etc.

proves fruitful nor agreeable to the tiller. The parts which have never been broke up nor had spade or plough in them, are most esteemed; and so fond are people of having the first tilling of a fresh spot, that I have known some hundreds of pounds given to obtain that pleasure.

Merryland is well water'd by a river, which takes its rise from a large reservoir or lake in the neighborhood called Vsca, and discharges itself with a most impetuous current and fearful cataract towards the terra firma near the entry of the great gulf; of this river I shall treat more particularly in another chapter.

There is a spacious canal which runs through the midst of this country, from one end almost to the other; it is so deep that authors affirm it has no bottom. I have often sounded it in many parts, and though I don't doubt but it has a bottom, I must own I never could reach it; perhaps, had my sounding-

Of the Air, Soil, Rivers, Canals, Etc.

line been a few fathoms longer, it might have reached the bottom.

We are told of Solomon's wells or cisterns at a place the Turks call Roselayne, which, like this canal, are reputed to be unfathomable; and the current tradition is, that they are filled from a subterraneous river, which that wise king, by his great sagacity, knew to run underground in that place. (See De Bruyn. Voyag. au Levant.) Whether this might not as properly be called Solomon's canal, I leave to the reader's judgment; it is certain that that wise king was no stranger to this country, but spent a great deal in improvements he made in several provinces of it.

All the superfluous moisture of the country is drained off through this canal, and it is likewise the conveyance of all provisions to the upper part of Merryland; all the seed sowed in that country is conveyed this way to the great storehouse at the upper end of it;

and, in short, there is no commodity imported into Merryland, but by this road; so that you may easily conceive it to be a place of great traffic. We may say of this canal, as the learned Doctor Cheyne says of the alimentary tube, "that it is, as it were, a common-sewer, which may be fouled or cleaned in various manners, and with great facility; it is wide, open, and reasonably strong."

The country is generally fertile enough, where duly manured; and some parts are so exceedingly fruitful as to bear two or three crops at a time; a Dutch traveller tells us there was once known to be as many crops as days in the year; but this I look upon as apocryphal. Other provinces are so utterly barren, that though a man should leave no stone unturned, but labor and toil forever, no seed will take root in them; yet so whimsical are many of the inhabitants, that they would choose one of these barren spots, rather than the more fertile ones; and indeed there is some reason for it, people having found by experience several great inconveniences by too fruitful a crop. 'Tis a lamentable thing for a man to have a large crop, when his circumstances can't afford houses to keep it in, or thatch to cover it; to let it perish would be infamous, and what can a poor man do? For he can't dispose of it immediately; it must be kept several years at great expense to him, before it is fit for the market, or capable of making the least return for his labor and expense. These are melancholy circumstances for the poor farmers;

> *Quæque ipse miserrima vidi,*
> *Et Quorum pars magna fui.**

This peculiarity has put some people on inventing means to prevent the seed taking root, or to destroy it before it comes to ma-

---

*———*Which I, alas! have seen, And deeply felt.*

turity; but such practices are only used by stealth, and not openly approved of; it is looked on as a bad practice, and we are told it was formerly punished with death.

It sounds odd, but it is no less true than strange, that many have been ruined and forced to run away by the greatness of their crop; and on the other hand, many are in a manner miserable and never satisfied because their spots prove barren. Strange contradiction in people's tempers! that what would be one man's delight, should be another man's torment!

We are told by Kercher of a mountain at Chekian, whose soil is of that quality, that it tames tigers, etc. This mountain, I presume, must be of the same kind of soil as Merryland, which in some degree has the power of taming the wildest creatures; nay, it will first make them in a manner mad, and tame them afterwards.

Of the Air, Soil, Rivers, Canals, Etc.

I shall conclude this chapter on the soil of Merryland by saying, "her valleys are like Eden, her hills like Lebanon, her springs as Pisgah, and her rivers as Jordan; that she is a paradise of pleasure and garden of delight."

Chapter iv

OF THE VAST EXTENT OF MERRYLAND,
ITS DIVISIONS AND PRINCIPAL
PLACES OF NOTE

The Arabian Geographical Lexicographer cited by Schultens in his geographical commentary at the end of his edition of *Sultan Salah'addin's Life,* very justly observes that the exact limits of this vast country are entirely unknown, the greatest traveller never having been able to discover its utmost bounds; and whoever attempts such a discovery, may properly enough be said to grope in the dark.

Besides those parts which are well known, and have been described by travellers, there are others of which we know but little, though some authors have pretended to be very exact and particular in their descriptions of them, for which they have no better authority than their own fancy and invention; and there are other parts of this country still unknown to us. It would swell this work too much, and be of little use to the reader, to take notice of every particular; I shall therefore content myself with mentioning such parts as are of most note, which are these:—

1st. At the end of the great canal toward the *terra firma* are two forts called Lba, between which everyone must necessarily pass that goes up the country, there being no other road. The fortifications are not very strong, though they have curtains, hornworks and ramparts; they have indeed sometimes defended the pass a pretty while, but were seldom or never known to hold out long against a close and vigorous attack.

2nd. Near these forts is the metropolis, called Cltrs; it is a pleasant place, much delighted in by the Queens of Merryland, and is their chief palace, or rather pleasure seat;

Of the Vast Extent of Merryland

it was at first but small, but the pleasure some of the queens have found in it has occasioned their extending its bounds considerably.

3rd. A little farther up the country are two other fortresses called Nmph, seated near the banks of the great river. These have sometimes made a stout resistance, against strong attacks and skilful engineers, and have endured a great deal of hardship in the assault, so that instances might be given of the most vigorous assailants being repulsed with great loss and confusion. On the other hand, they have often been known to give way upon the first slight attack, and admit the assailants without any opposition.

4th. At the upper end of the great canal, mentioned in the former chapter, is the great treasury or storehouse, called Utrs, of which Plautus gives this description:

> *Item esse reor*
> *Mare ut est; quod das devorat, nunquam*

Of the Vast Extent of Merryland

abundat,
Des quantum vis.*

This storehouse is of a very particular structure; in shape it somewhat resembles one of our common pint bottles, with the neck downwards. It is so admirably well contrived that its dimensions are always adapted to its contents; for as the store contained in it increases, so the bounds are extended in proportion; and when it is quite empty, or but little in it, it contracts or diminishes proportionably, and that without any art or assistance.

5th. Another part of this country, often mentioned by authors, is Hmn, about which there have been great controversies and disputes among the learned, some denying there ever was such a place, others positively

---

* ———————*Semblance meet*
Of the wide ocean, which ingulfs whate'er
Within its circuits falls; in its abyss
Absorbing great, or little, as it chances:
Gorge it to the brim, strait it all devours!
And craves for more.

affirming to have seen it. For my part, after the nicest inquiry I could make, I never could discover anything satisfactory about it; and most travellers now agree, that if it ever did exist, it is utterly defaced by time or accident, so that in these latter ages no footstep of it is to be found; agreeable to that saying of the poet:

Etiam ipsæ periere Ruinæ.*

6th. Here I must not omit to mention a famous pleasant mount called Mnsvnrs, which overlooks the whole country; and, lastly, round the borders of Merryland is a spacious forest, which (as Mr. Chamberlayne says of the forests in England) "seems to have been preserved for the pleasure of variety and diversion of hunting."

These are the principal places observed by travellers; and to give a more complete geographical description of this country, I in-

* ———————*No mark of such a thing now seen.*

Of the Vast Extent of Merryland

tended to have added a map of it; but recollecting that it would considerably enhance the price of the book, I choose rather to refer the curious reader to a map of Merryland, curiously engraven on copper plate, and published some years ago by the learned Mr. Moriceau, who was a great traveller in that country, and surveyed it with tolerable exactness. There the reader may see all the noted places and divisions laid down exactly as they are situated; and here I must in justice to the learned Sir R. M. acknowledge, that his late contrived model or machine is a very ingenious invention, which gives a better idea of Merryland than can possibly be done by the best maps, or any written description.

Chapter V

OF THE ANCIENT AND MODERN INHABITANTS,
THEIR MANNERS, CUSTOMS, ETC.

MERRYLAND is well known to have been inhabited soon after the Fall, and Adam was the first adventurer who planted a colony in this fruitful and delicious country. After him the Patriarchs were industrious tillers of the soil. David and Solomon were often there, and many modern kings and princes have honored this country with their royal presence and protection. King Charles II in particular was in close alliance with it, and it flourished exceedingly in his days. Nor has it been slighted by his royal successors, some of whom have taken great delight in it, and their councils have sometimes been influenced by the situation of affairs in Merryland. We have had ministers who preferred

Of the Ancient and Modern Inhabitants

its welfare to that of their own country, and bishops who would not be displeased to have a small bishopric in Merryland. At present the inhabitants of this country are very numerous, and composed of people of all degrees, all religions, and of all nations.

As to the manners of the inhabitants, though they are sometimes very low and despicable, being soon dispirited and dejected by violent exercise; yet, when in good spirit, they are very strong and vigorous, and when bent upon their pleasure, are very bold and daring. They are much addicted to pleasure and diversion in private, notwithstanding they affect great gravity and restraint in public.

They are vastly ticklish, and so fond of it, that when they can get nobody to please them that way, they will tickle themselves. They are naturally given to love freedom and liberty, prone to change and variety, much given to dissembling and flattery, and greatly addicted to venery; they have little esteem of frugality or economy, but spend all they can, and glory who spends most. They pride themselves much in their stiff and stately carriage, and cannot have a greater compliment paid them, than by comparing them to the Behemoth, of whom it is said in Job, that his strength is in his loins, and he moveth his tail like a cedar.

Homer gives a beautiful description of their boldness and bravery in an engagement, and with what intrepidity they make an attack; which Mr. Pope has translated thus:

He foams, he glares, he bounds against them all;
And if he falls, his courage makes him fall.

One remarkable custom of the natives is, that the moment they come into the world, they leave the particular spot they were born in, and never after return to it, but wander about till they are 14 or 15 years old, at which

Of the Ancient and Modern Inhabitants

age they generally look out for some other spot of Merryland, and take possession of it the first opportunity; but to enter again in that part they were born in is looked on as an infamous crime, and severely punishable by law; yet some have been hardy enough to do it.

There are some whimsical ceremonies commonly observed by people when they take possession of any part of this country, such as prostrating themselves on their faces, and muttering many ejaculations in praise of the spot they have chosen; then laying their hand on it by way of taking seisin; then they plough it, and fall to laboring the soil with all their might, the laborer being generally on his knees. Some indeed work standing; but the other way is the most common.

Another thing very remarkable is the custom observed commonly at all merry-makings among the men when over a bottle; instead of toasting their mistresses, they begin with drinking a health to Merryland; and it is a known rule that this must be always drank in a bumper. If anyone refuses he is looked on as a sneaking fellow. To keep them in mind of this duty I have seen the following verses inscribed on their cups and glasses under the word Merryland:

> *Hic quicunque legis nomen Amabile*
> *Pleno lætoque Cyatho salutem libes,*
> *Sic tibi res amatoriæ prospere cedant,*
> *Tua sic coronet vota Cupido.**

As to the genius of the inhabitants it may be observed the liberal arts are here in the greatest repute; here experimental philosophy has been improved to a wonder; physic and surgery have flourished exceedingly; and

---

* *Whoever takes this glass in hand,*
And reads thereon dear Merryland,
Fill it sparkling to the top,
Toast the health, and tope it up;
So may all thy vows be heard,
When at Venus' shrine preferr'd;
So may thy fair one gentle prove,
And cupid ever crown thy love.

no country is better stocked with divines. And for merchandising, the great wealth arising from trade in some provinces is a plain proof and demonstration that traffic is carried on in Merryland with great success.

Here I must not omit taking notice that this country has produced and inspired great numbers of excellent poets, and in return, they have in many of their works expressed their great regard for the country, and celebrated its praises with the utmost gratitude and affection. One of them says:

> *Hic ætatis nostræ primordia novit,*
> *Annos fælices, lætitæque dies:*
> *Hic locus ingenuus pueriles imbuit annos*
> *Artibus, et nostræ laudis origo fuit.**

---

* *Here my first breath with happy stars was drawn;*
Here my glad years and all my joys begun:
In gradual knowledge, here my mind increased;
Here the first sparks of glory fir'd my breast.

Chapter vi

OF THE PRODUCT AND COMMODITIES, SUCH AS FISH, FOWLS, BEASTS, PLANTS, ETC.

THOUGH this country is so plentifully watered, by so fine a river and canal, it is but indifferently stored with fish; yet when a stranger comes to Merryland he would imagine by the smell of the air that the country abounded with ling or red-herrings; as we are told the river Tyssa in Hungary smells of fish; so strong is this smell sometimes, that it is very offensive; but here are no such fish to be seen. Cod indeed are often found about the lower end of the great canal, and crabs in plenty on its banks. I never heard of any other fish in Merryland, except muscles, gudgeons in abundance, some dabs, and a few maids; these last are rarely met with, and it is the difficulty of catching them, I suppose,

Of the Product and Commodities

makes them much valued by persons of nice taste. I have indeed heard of a mackerel being found here by Mr. R., a surgeon of Plymouth; but this was purely accidental, it being only one single mackerel brought to Merryland by a young woman merely for the sake of trying an experiment. However, this scarcity of fish is the less to be lamented, as in this country a flesh diet is most delighted in, and with that they generally are pretty well supplied.

For fowls, here are cocks, wagtails, buzzards, widgeons and gulls, besides tomtits, which being small insignificant creatures are of no esteem, and capons, which are likewise held in great disrepute.

Of beasts, here are plenty of asses, some bears, dromedaries and mules, and many sly old foxes. I have heard likewise of baboons, monkeys, and spaniels; but as it is unnatural to find them here, I believe it is likewise more uncommon than is reported. I know it has

Of the Product and Commodities

been strongly insisted on by several learned men (some of them great travellers in Merryland) that rabbits have been bred in that country, and they expected great profits from a warren they pretended to have lately discovered; but, after a great noise made about it, all came to nothing.

As for the commodities of the mineral and vegetable kind, here are a few of each which I shall take notice of, as far as my observation and memory serve me.

Of the mineral kind, the blue or Roman vitriol (which is of great use to eat away proud flesh) is often found on the borders of this country; and it is observed the provinces, where this is found, are generally unwholesome.

There have been instances of gold and silver discovered here, nor is the country destitute of precious stones, here being a kind very much esteemed, though very common to be met with on the surface; so fond are they of them that a man would be looked on with contempt in Merryland if he had not at least two of them, which they always carry about them in a purse; they contribute very much to the fruitfulness of the soil.

Of the vegetable kind, here is rue in great plenty; carrots are no strangers to this soil, but are much used; here is some true-love and sweet-marjoram, and the plant called maiden-hair; but the last is very scarce. Here is no scarcity of several kinds of simples, of which they make great profit.

There is a plant of the submarine kind which delights much in this soil: the end of it resembles the red coral, and partakes much of its virtue; it is highly esteemed in Merryland, and is undoubtedly a great sweetener; it being frequently applied very successfully to cure sharp and sour humors. This plant yields a whitish viscid juice, which, when taken inwardly, has a bad effect on some people, causing a large tumor in the umbilical regions, which is not got rid of again without great pain. But there are many on whom it never has that effect, let them take ever so great a quantity of it. It is generally reckoned an excellent cosmetic, "giving a most inexpressible resplendent brightness to the whole countenance, and causes sparkling life, spirit and juvenile bloom to reign in every feature." It may properly enough be called the coral-plant, as it resembles it in several particulars. Mr. Boyle affirms of the nature and generation of coral, that whilst it grows, it is often soft and succulent, and propagates its species. And Kircher was informed by the divers that the coral would sometimes let fall a spermatic juice, which lighting on a proper body, produced another coral. The same may be said of the plant above mentioned.

Another submarine plant is said to be found in Merryland, of the sponge kind, the name of which I have forgotten. They use it not only as a cleanser, but also as an antidote

Of the Product and Commodities

against the bad effects of the juice above mentioned.

Here are flowers in great plenty, but not much to be commended, either for fragrancy or beauty. They are not variegated, nor is there any great diversity of colors; red and white are most common. Some naturalists have imagined these flowers to be of a poisonous quality; but that notion is now sufficiently exploded, and it is observed, if they happen not to spring in their due season, the country generally proves unhealthy and barren.

As for manufactures, I never heard of any in Merryland worth mentioning, except those for pins and needles, which are made in great plenty in some of the most trading provinces, and are famous for their exquisite sharpness.

Chapter vii

OF THE RARITIES, CURIOSITIES, ETC.

THE great river mentioned in the third chapter is very remarkable; the water is warm and brackish, and does not run in a constant stream like other rivers, but the current stops every day for hours together; and without observing any regular period, it all of a sudden falls a-running again with great rapidity. This river (like the river Ness in Scotland, and the lake of Drontheim in Norway) never freezes in the hardest frosts, but always retains its natural heat; and has another remarkable quality, like that of the river Adonis near Byblus in Phœnicia, which at certain seasons appears bloody, as we are told in Maundrel's journey from Aleppo to Jerusalem.

Of the Rarities, Curiosities, Etc.

The canal, already noticed in the third chapter, deserves to be ranked among the curiosities of this country, not only for its wonderful depth, which is said to be unfathomable; but for another extraordinary quality, no less surprising; for as it is reported of some lakes in China, that throwing anything into them causes a storm, so on the contrary many violent storms have been appeased, if not entirely laid, by throwing into this canal a handsome sprig of the coral plant mentioned in the sixth chapter. This famous canal answers the description given in the atlas, of a lake near Le Besse in Brittany, which is so deep, it never could be sounded; and in a hollow place near it, a noise is heard like thunder.

Among the rarities may likewise justly be reckoned that wonderful mountain on the confines of Merryland, which at some seasons begins to extend its dimensions both in height and bigness, and increases its bulk so considerably, that it is esteemed one of the most admirable works of nature; after it has continued swelling thus gradually for some months, it will fall again all at once, and be reduced to its former compass. This swelling is generally the forerunner of a dear year; and therefore some of the poorer sort, who are not bound to their farms by lease, take the alarm at this ominous swelling, and fly the country, as soon as they perceive it.

There are two other pleasant little mountains called Bby, which though at some distance from Merryland, have great affinity with that country, and are properly reckoned as an appendage to it. These little mountains are exactly alike, and not far from each other, having a pleasant valley between them; on the top of each is a fine fountain, that yields a very wholesome liquor much esteemed, especially by the younger sort of people. These fountains are often quite dry; but it is observed they seldom fail to run plentifully

Of the Rarities, Curiosities, Etc.

after the swelling of the other mountain beforementioned, and they have in some degree the same faculty of rising and falling; so that it is not without good reason, philosophers have imagined there is a secret communication between these places.

But of all the curiosities, nothing deserves our notice so much as a small animal, somewhat of the serpentine kind, known by the name of Pntl; it is often found plunging about in the great canal, which is the place it mostly delights in; so wonderful is this creature that it well deserves a particular description in this place, and though it be but small, I may say of it, as is said of the Leviathan, "I will not conceal his parts, nor his power, nor his comely proportion; he maketh the deep to boil like a pot; he is king over all the children of pride." This animal has neither legs nor feet, but, by the vast strength of its muscles, has a power of erecting itself, so as to stand almost upright.

That learned physician and philosopher, Dr. Cheyne, seems to have had this in view when he said, "The animal body is nothing but a compages or contexture of pipes; an hydraulic machine, filled with a liquor of such a nature as was transfused into it by its parents, or is changed into by the nature of the food it is nourished with, and is ever afterwards good, bad, or indifferent, as these two sources have sent it forth." They are only of the male kind, and yet propagate their species very plentifully. This may seem very strange at first sight, to those who have not thrown off the material incrustation that entangles and fetters the full exercise and penetration of their natural powers, which are tied down, sopited, and fettered by the manner of our origin; but anyone who will consult the learned author beforementioned, will find he very logically proves that in all animals "originally there must have been no difference of sexes, because at last in their restored state there will be none. And that it is highly probable, the female was but a secondary intention, or a buttress to a falling edifice."

They are of different sizes, from six to seven or eight inches in height, when full grown, and from four to six in circumference; there are some indeed of much larger dimensions, but very rarely to be met with; and there are others much less, but they are of little or no value; those of a middling size are observed to be more lively and vigorous than the larger sort, who like the grenadiers in a regiment, are not able to make so long and frequent marches as the battalion men, the latter being for the most part better set and nimbler, as being furnished with a greater plenty of spirits.

One thing is very remarkable of these animals, that either sleeping or waking, when they lie down, they immediately contract themselves to one-third of their length and bigness, and grow so flagged and limber, one would scarce think they had ever been enabled to stand; but when they are roused up and in full vigor they are very stately, and much admired for their portly mien. Here I must beg leave to refer once more to the above quoted author, who tells us, "This spiritual animal body, at first divinely organized, may be rolled up, folded together, and contracted in this state of its duration, into an infinitely small *punctum saliens,* into a miniature of miniature in infinitum, and proceeding in a diverging series, and progressive gradation, that in due time it may be fit to be nourished and increased by the juices of the proper female." In pursuit of their prey, no creature can be more keen, and they rush on it with great eagerness. Their skin is of a swarthy complexion, and hangs so loose about their shoulders, that it frequently serves as a hood to draw up quite over its head and face, or rather the head shrinks into the skin as a snail pulls in his horns and head into his shell. The face of this creature is of a reddish complexion, and most delicately soft to the touch; they are flat nosed, and have no eyes, but find their way by instinct. They have no bones, but are all muscles and flesh, which properly prepared and taken inwardly, is very refreshing and nourishing. It is reckoned a specific for the green-sickness, and many other feminine disorders; and is a medicine so wonderfully pleasant and easy in its operation, that the nicest palate or weakest constitution may take it with delight, and so innocent, that it is administered to women with child with great safety.

Chapter viii

OF THE GOVERNMENT OF MERRYLAND

THE government of this country is monarchical, and absolute in the highest degree. As the French have their salique law, by which all females are excluded from the throne, so the contrary, Merryland may be said to be entirely under female government, there being an absolute queen over each particular province, whose power is unlimited; no tyrants have ever required a more servile and blind submission than the queens of Merryland. Herodianus (Lib. 4, cap. 3) says, "They treated their subjects as the meanest of slaves, and scarce as men, while they put themselves on a level with the immortal Gods." There are numberless instances of the vast power of these queens, the conquests they have made, and the many cunning and crafty methods they have used to obtain their ends; but as I do not pretend to write their history, I must not here enlarge on that subject. Few of these queens but have some favorite or prime minister, and when they are well satisfied with his abilities and behavior, they will suffer themselves to be governed in a great measure by his advice; but alas! there are some who, though they have abundance of able ministers, will never be ruled by any of them, are always varying and changing, turning out their greatest favorites, for no other reason in the world, but to show their power, and gratify their inconstant tempers; admitting a new favorite every day, as if variety was their greatest delight. Such are the caprices of these queens, and so uncertain the prosperity of their ablest ministers. Besides their capriciousness, many of them are also justly accused for their greedy and insatiable tempers, forcing their subjects to labor, drudge and toil without ceasing, to satisfy their voracious appetites. Some few able-bodied men have indeed made shift to do their work, and these, it must be owned, meet with good encouragement; though they are kept to hard labor, they get a comfortable subsistence as their reward. I have known some of them well-clothed and fed, and in a very thriving way; but not every one is qualified by nature to go through so much fatigue.

Some of these queens have deserved the worst of characters, and are recorded for their infamy in the works of the Greek and Roman satirists. But our British Juvenal, in an excellent Latin satire lately published, has given us so lively a picture of one of them, that I cannot forbear transcribing four lines, which excel all I have ever met with, either in the ancients or moderns.

Saga petit juvenes, petit innuptasque puellas;
Vel taurum peteret, veneris quoque mille figuras,

Of the Government of Merryland

Mille modos meditans, Ætas in crimina vires,
Datque animos: crescunt anni, crescitque libido.*
                                    SCAMNUM.

As to the Military Government of this country, I cannot pretend to say much, as I am not acquainted with their several rules; but I have observed in general, that soldiers are well esteemed and encouraged, and there are no complaints against red coats in Merryland, however they may be disapproved of in other countries. Their naval forces are likewise very considerable, and of great service to the country, being a set of lusty fellows, always willing to work when ashore, and never backward in spending their all, for the service of the particular queen under whose jurisdiction they live.

It would no doubt be very acceptable to

---

* *The witch seduces youth and virgins pure,*
And would a bull, could she the weight endure;
She tries all postures lust has e'er contriv'd,
And of her own adds many more beside;
Her crimes, by age, have strength and courage found,
And as her years increase, her lusts abound.

Of the Government of Merryland

the reader, if after the civil and military, I could give him any particular account of the ecclesiastical government of this country; and it is with the greatest concern that I am not able to gratify his curiosity; for the clergy endeavor to keep it a secret as much as possible among themselves, being a mystery they think improper to be divulged among the laity; and though I could mention some particulars on this subject, which have accidentally come to my knowledge, I must desire to be excused, being very unwilling to give offence to a body of men, for whom I have the greatest veneration, and to some of whom I have been particularly obliged for their kind assistance and recommendation, which contributed much to the pleasure I have enjoyed in Merryland. I shall therefore say no more of the ecclesiastical government, but only observe in general (and I hope without offence) that there are many bishoprics in this country, the exact number I cannot pretend to guess at, nor how far their several jurisdictions reach. Of the inferior clergy here are such abundance, that they may, on a modest computation, be reckoned to enjoy more than the tithe of all Merryland.

Chapter ix

OF THE RELIGION OF MERRYLAND

CHRISTIANITY was first planted here, in all probability, in the earliest ages of the church; at present no country can boast of more religions, and yet no part of Christendom may be truly said to be less religious than this. Here we may see all sects and parties (all religions being embraced) and yet that which the apostle calls the pure and undefiled religion before God and the Father, is as little, if not less thought on here, than in any Christian country whatsoever.

Image worship (to the shame of the country be it spoken) is a vice they are not entirely free of: for it is well known, too many of the queens of Merryland have a particular veneration for a certain image, made in re-

Of the Religion of Merryland

semblance of the coral plant mentioned in the sixth chapter; to this they often pay their devotions with the greatest privacy; the ceremony consists of various emotions and agitations of the body, and manual performances, which my abhorrence of the idolatrous custom forbids me to describe more particularly. 'Tis much better my readers should be kept in ignorance of such shameful actions, which all men must detest, than by any further description be informed how to practice them.

Here are Popish missionaries in great plenty, and by that means the Roman Catholic religion is pretty much propagated, they being very laborious and indefatigable. Quakers, Presbyterians, Independents, and of late the Methodists, have been great laborers in these parts, though not so professedly and openly perhaps as some others. It is to be lamented that so many sects are tolerated, especially considering the dangerous heats and flames that are kindled in the country by

Of the Religion of Merryland

the intemperate zeal of so many different sects. In short, there is no sect whatever, but has found footing in Merryland; and it is hard to say which of them all is the most established. One thing is pretty remarkable, in which they all agree with that excellent litany of our church, all of them joining in that prayer, to strengthen such as do stand, to comfort and help the weak, and raise up those that fall.

Chapter x

OF THE LANGUAGE

THE same may be said of the language used in Merryland, as Mr. Gordon says of the Japanese tongue: "It is very polite and copious, abounding with many synonymous words, which are commonly used according to the nature of the subject, as also the quality, age, and sex, both of the speaker and the person to whom the discourse is directed." There is somewhat very sweet and emphatic in the language, and at the same time it may be said, they have the least need of it of any people, for they have the art of communicating their sentiments very plainly by their eyes and actions, so that mute persons can (if I may be allowed the expression) speak intelligibly by their eyes; and this kind is often

Of the Language

used with better success than the finest speeches.

To confirm this I beg leave to refer the curious reader to the following quotation from a learned author, who says, "Mirantur Oculi, adamant, concupiscunt, Amoris, Iræ, Furoris, Misericordiæ, Ultionis Indices sunt; in Audacia profiliunt, in Reverentia subsident, in Amore blandiuntur, in Dio efferantur, gaudente animo hilares subsident, in Cogitatione ac Cura quiescunt, quasi cum Mente simul intenti, etc."* (LAUR. *Lib. de Sens. Org.* 11, *Cap.* 3.)

They have likewise some particular motions of the tongue, which very emphatically express their meaning, without uttering any articulate sound, and is frequently more successful than the finest flowers of elocution.

---

* The eyes may properly be term'd the index of the soul, inasmuch as they discover her various passions of admiration, fondness, desire, love, anger, fury, pity and revenge; when daring, they dart forth; when obsequious they submissively recline; when enamour'd, they soothe; when at liberty, they roam; plainly demonstrating when the mind is exhilarated, and when overwhelmed with anxiety and care, etc.

Of the Language

It is much to be lamented that nobody has given us a grammar of the Merryland language; it would be very useful to the world, and I do not despair of prevailing on the modesty of a learned orator to undertake it, who has already obliged the world with half a score of other grammars, and is universally allowed to be as well qualified for compiling this, as he was for those.

Chapter xi

OF THE SEVERAL TENURES, ETC.

THERE are perhaps as many kinds of tenures in Merryland as in any country whatever, and it would be as difficult as it is needless to enumerate them all. Some holding by tail-special, some by tail-general, some by knights-service, some in fee-simple, others only during pleasure, and others by lease for life. This last is pretty common, and though not perhaps the best tenure, is the most encouraged by law, and therefore shall first be treated of. The circumstances attending it are very singular, and worth observation.

When a man resolves to take a spot in Merryland by this tenure, he makes the best agreement he can with the proprietor of the farm, and the terms being concluded on, public notice is given, that he designs speedily to enter into possession, that any person, who has just objection to it, may forbid it before it is too late. You must know there are several lawful objections such as the farm being engaged before to another, or the man having already another farm on his hands (for none are allowed to hold two at a time by this tenure) his being any ways pre-engaged, or having any incapacity to manure his farm, etc. If no objection be made (to avoid which, they sometimes purchase a license, which dispenses with the ceremony of giving public notice) then the lease for life is executed in the following manner.

The officer, whose business it is (and of which there is one in each parish) reads a short panegyric on farming, setting forth its original institution and use, the great importance and honor of that state, with proper precautions not to take it in hand unadvisedly, lightly or wantonly, and requires the man (as he shall answer at the dreadful Day of Judgment) to confess freely, if he knows any lawful impediment, why he should not proceed in taking his lease. Then the man makes a solemn promise that he will take the farm according to law, that he will keep it whether it prove good or bad, and forsaking all others keep only unto that for life; the officer then gives his blessing to the undertaking, prays for the success, and then sings a song, setting forth the happiness of farming, and great promises of fruitfulness.

The ceremony being ended, the man takes possession of his lot, and commonly begins to till it before he sleeps; and whatever season of the year it be he generally continues tilling and laboring hard for the first few days, till he is tired, and forced to take some respite.

These long leases have been the ruin of many a substantial farmer, for people are too apt to engage in a hurry, without due consideration of the consequence, or competent knowledge of the goodness of the farm, which frequently proves to be a stubborn soil, and makes the poor farmer soon repent his bargain; but there is no remedy, the man is bound, and must drudge on for life. This inconvenience has deterred many from ever taking leases; and others, who have rashly been bound to a hard bargain, when they find there is no remedy, have been so discouraged that they become ill husbands, growing quite indolent and negligent of their farm; and though they cannot throw up their leases, they will let their farms lie fallow, and clandestinely take another that is more agreeable to them.

There are many people who never will venture to take a farm by the tenure before-mentioned, but choose rather to hold as tenants at will or during pleasure, and though they pay a dear rate, they have this advantage, that whenever they do not like their farm they can immediately quit it and take

Of the Several Tenures, Etc.

another; there is little danger of one of these farms lying long unoccupied, for if one man leave it to-day, another takes it to-morrow.

Those who hold by knights-service in the courtesy of Merryland thrive generally very well, and reap good profit by their labor, especially if they be able and painstaking men; let the soil be ever so long worn, and out of heart, yet they will make something of it.

There is a great deal of ground in Merryland which lies common, and this is so bad that let a man sow ever so much seed in it, it seldom produces anything better than briars and thorns. This ground is not worth enclosing, though some people have been fools enough to attempt it.

There is one inconvenience attends most of the farms in Merryland, for it is a difficult matter to fence or enclose them so securely, but the neighbors, who are very apt to watch all opportunities, may easily break into them; and it is surprising, where there is so much common, and a great deal of good pasture to be got at easy rates, that people should be so fond of breaking into their neighbors' enclosures, where if they are caught, and prosecuted, they run a risk of paying very severely, the law being very strict in these cases; and juries are so apt to give the plaintiff immoderate great damages, that I have known a man cast in several thousand pounds damages for a small trespass on a farm, which was little better than common, and which the owner would gladly have sold the fee-simple of for a hundredth part of the money.

Chapter xii

OF THE HARBORS, BAYS, CREEKS, SANDS, ROCKS, AND OTHER DANGEROUS PLACES; WITH THE SETTINGS AND FLOWINGS OF THE TIDES AND CURRENTS; ALSO DIRECTIONS FOR STRANGERS STEERING SAFE INTO MERRYLAND.

To recite all the bays, creeks, etc., would be an endless piece of work; and it is as impossible to point out all the rocks which people have split on when bound for Merryland. But I shall here give the reader the best directions I can to pilot him safe to this charming country, by describing the two courses that are most commonly steered, and leave it to everyone to choose which suits best with his inclination or convenience.

They who go by the upper course make first for that part of the continent called Lps, where they generally bring to, and salute the fort; and sometimes it is required that they pay the customs and duties here before they are allowed to proceed further; but this is not always demanded. Then if you find the wind favorable, steer along shore to the Bby Mountains, where there is good sailing; and if you meet with no storm, but find it calm and quiet, you may thence safely venture to run on with the tide, and push in boldly for the harbor. But if you find rough and tempestuous weather, as sometimes happens at touching at Bby, and the tide strong against you, it is best to lie by till the storm is appeased, and a fairer prospect offers itself of a prosperous voyage; nor should you be discouraged by every little squall which you may meet with at this place, for generally these squalls, though they seem violent at first, soon blow over without much damage.

Some people prefer the lower course, which is, at once to run in boldly up the straits of Tibia, with the coxadext bearing close on the larboard bow, and so run ahead, directly as the current carries you, into the harbor; and indeed when the trade winds set in, this course cannot fail.

In either of these courses it is best to be provided with a good forestaff, kept in such order, as to be always ready for use at a moment's warning. I have known some people, for want of this instrument being in readiness, make a very unsuccessful voyage, and been put back again, to their great disappointment, when they were just at the entry of the harbor. It is also proper to make frequent observations and soundings; but, as Mr. Collin says in his Coasting Pilot, "the thing principally to be observed is the setting of the tide, which often alters the course, to the disappointment of the mariner; for when you sail close upon a wind, if the tide takes you on the weather-bough, you will fall too much to leeward of your expectation, and if on the lee-bough, it carries you too much to windward." The same author very justly observes, "There is generally so great an indraught of the tide that in little wind or a calm you will be drawn in to admiration."

Though the tide is generally very favorable and sets into the harbor, it is to be noted that at the time of spring-tides, which only flow for four or five days, once in a month, the current then runs strong out, and it is best to lie by till the spring is over, though some people make no scruple of going in when the spring-tides are at the height.

There are people who, instead of steering either of these courses, incline sometimes to go about by the windward passage, but this I do not approve; in most circumstances indeed this is done more for sake of variety than conveniency.

Different pilots have given us variety of directions and showed many ways of steering safely to Merryland; among others, that ingenious pilot, M. Aratine, has published several charts, with the different bearings, etc., to which I refer the curious reader, rather

Of the Harbors, Bays, Creeks, Etc.

than swell this chapter any more; and indeed I do not see any great necessity for many directions, the voyage not being so difficult, but what a blind man may almost find his way thither, by one course or another; or should any one be at a loss when he comes to the coast of Merryland, it's ten to one but he will find a pilot to help him into harbor, they being ready enough to oblige strangers in that way, as I myself found in my first voyage, when I was very young and not expert in these matters. It is remarkable, that when our mariners come near the coast in other parts of the world, they wish for light nights that they may see the shore, etc., but in the voyages to Merryland, they meet with no inconvenience from the dark, but find it generally favors them, and helps into harbor with less trouble than broad daylight.

After you have fairly entered the mouth of the harbor, go up as far as you can, and come to an anchor, veering out as much cable as possible; the more you veer, the better you will sail. The chief thing is to beware of anchoring in foul ground; for here is some much gruffer than others, and a great deal so very bad that it will soon spoil the best of cables; the sandy or grey ground are not good to anchor in, the brown is best, in my opinion. But as people cannot always have their choice, they must be contented with such as they can get.

Now, having brought my reader to anchor in this pleasant harbor, I conclude with wishing him all the delight Merryland can afford. I have endeavored to conduct him safe, and give him a full view of this delicious country, without the danger of waves, tempests, or shipwreck; and if he reaps either pleasure or profit from my labor, I shall think the pains I have taken to compile this short treatise very well rewarded.

FINIS